© 1997 Owl Records Ltd
Published by Geddes & Grosset, an imprint of
Children's Leisure Products Limited,
David Dale House, New Lanark, ML11 9DJ, Scotland,
for Owl Records Ltd, Dublin, Ireland

First printed 1997
Reprinted 1998, 1999, 2000

ISBN 1 85534 755 5

Printed and bound in Slovenia

IRISH LEGENDS

ST BRIGID'S Cloak

Retold by Reg Keating
Illustrated by Heather McKay

Tarantula Books

Brigid was the daughter of a wealthy man.

She was also his slave, just as her mother had been.

She spent her days cooking, cleaning and washing.

She fed pigs and milked cows on her father's farm.

In summer, she tilled the crops and harvested the corn.

Even though she worked from dawn till dusk, she never complained.

Brigid lived at the time of Saint Patrick.

She listened to Saint Patrick and became a Christian.

Brigid's father was a Pagan. He could not understand Brigid's wish to serve God.

When Brigid was eighteen, she no longer worked as a slave.

Her father hoped to find a husband for her. But Brigid's mind was made up. She did not want a husband.

S he wanted to spend her life working for God.

She spent all her time looking after the poor, the sick and the elderly.

Soon the news about Brigid spread far and wide.

Young girls from all over Ireland came to join her. They wanted to be like Brigid. They wanted to help her in doing her good works.

Soon there were too many girls for all of them to live on Brigid's father's farm.

"Where can we find places for all these young girls?" Brigid's mother asked anxiously.

"And how can we feed them all?" asked her father.

"Don't worry," said Brigid. "God will provide for them."

Brigid's father did not understand. "Your God does not own any land," he said. "You will need land to feed all these young girls."

The King of Leinster owns all the land around here. He will not give even the smallest piece of it to you," he told her.

"My God is more powerful than you know," said Brigid. "He will persuade the King of Leinster to give me some land."

"Ha!" laughed her father. "Fat chance you have of getting some land from the King of Leinster. He is the meanest man in all of Ireland."

B rigid was not down-hearted.
With four of her young girls, she set
off to find the King of Leinster.

When she reached the Curragh of
Kildare, she met the King who was out
hunting.

The King dismounted from his horse.

He approached Brigid and her friends.

"Good day, ladies," he said. "How may I
help you?"

Brigid explained her need for some land.

S he told the King that the spot where they stood was the perfect place for their new home.

It was beside a forest where they could collect firewood.

There was a lake nearby that would provide them with water.

The land was flat and fertile. It would provide good feeding for their cattle.

The King looked at her and laughed.

He would not give away even the worst of his land.

He most certainly would not give away some of his best land.

He immediately refused Brigid's request.

"The forest is my best hunting ground," said the King. "And the lake is the best of the fishing waters in all of Ireland."

Brigid was not down-hearted. She said a little prayer to God.

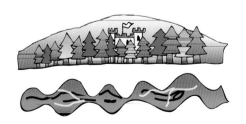

S he asked Him to soften the King's heart.

Then she smiled at the King and said, "Will you give me as much land as my cloak will cover?"

The King was amused. He thought it was a joke. Brigid's cloak was so small that it would cover only a tiny piece of land.

"Of what possible use could such a small piece of land be?" he asked.

"I could feed all my animals and look after all my girls on such a piece of land," replied Brigid.

The King again laughed out loud. Just for fun, he agreed.

With that, Brigid removed her cloak. She spread it smoothly and evenly on the ground.

Then she asked each of her four friends to hold a corner of the cloak. When they each held a corner, Brigid instructed them to walk in opposite directions.

One walked to the north and one to the south. Another walked to the east while the fourth walked to the west.

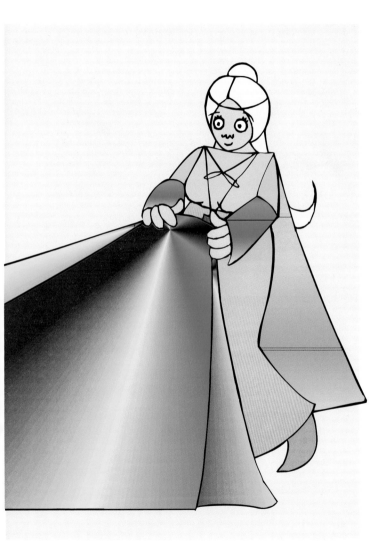

The cloak immediately began to grow in size.

The King was astonished.

The cloak grew and grew until it covered many acres of land.

Some of the King's hunting party fled in terror. Others realised that Brigid had Divine power.

They fell to the ground before her. They promised her and her girls money, food and provisions.

The King knelt before Brigid. "From this moment on," he said, "anything you ask for, I will gladly give to you."

Soon afterwards, the King became a Christian and gave much to the poor.

Brigid's miracle of the cloak was the first of many miracles that she worked for the people of Ireland.